MW00809847

Piñata Moon

By Torran Anderson

The events and conversations in this book have been set down to the best of the author's ability, although some names and details have been changed to protect the privacy of individuals. Some parts have been fictionalized in varying degrees, for various purposes.

Copyright © 2019 by Torran Anderson

All rights reserved. No part of this book may be reproduced or used in any manner without written permission of the copyright owner except for the use of quotations in a book review.

ISBN 978-1-7337809-0-2 (paperback)
ISBN 978-1-7337809-1-9 (ebook)

www.torrananderson.com

Saddling the Toyota Corolla, 6:20 PM

We race across I-10,
past stolen shopping carts and cactus wrens,
Aztec murals, and gas station parking lots.
Past apartment complexes and the wildlife museum,
full of dead animals,
stuffed and posed as though they're living.

We flee to the sunset,
sweat stains on the Corolla's seats.
Hands in the wind, eyes open,
having changed out of our ironed funeral clothes.
Lowrider clouds cruise the sky
and scrape against dusty peaks.

Windows down, speakers rattling,
bugs buzz in, light slants in,
the cactus thorns' illuminated halos,
angelic in their prickly auras.
Saguaros stand with their arms thrown up in the air
as if a hooligan snuck behind them and yelled,
"Stick em up."

At Gates Pass, we turn the corner slowly,
make a hard left and creep down

into the open valley.
The yellow lines
on the asphalt
change to
dash—dash—dash.

Waiting for the moon
to rise and take over the sky,
the only one
I can talk to
now that J.
is gone.

@themoonforreal
Even if you don't admit it…I know what you're thinking.

Because I Wonder If I'd Do What J. Did

I make a list of tiny moments I enjoy about living,
to remember the things that make me happy
even if they're small reasons:

1. The dripping cool desert after it rains.

2. Videos of elephant reunions.

3. When mom used to sing to me, "I see the
   moon, and the moon sees me."

Waiting for the Monsoon

Those who died too soon
don't do
sentimental things
like you imagine.
They play old arcade games
unnostalgically,
for top score;
they scrounge together
loose change for postcards;
check email; pump air in their tires
and try and pass
as those with breath,
but they cannot.
They wait to come alive
after the rain passes,
believing they could
leap into flesh
straight from their bones.

We all dance
when it rains,
though not all of us
noticeably so,
maybe just

a sigh,
an inhale of air,
crisp dew
dripping from
creosote bushes,
wooden saguaro ribs
soaked to the bone,
dust laundered from
the breeze.
The land
so ripe
you cannot help
but feel
you
are blooming.

@themoonforreal
I'm not your narrator, there's no Morgan Freeman voice-over to explain what's happening. You have to figure it out.

My Life as an Internet Search

If you click back through parties
we stumbled through,
search back through the girls I didn't kiss,
took back the words I wrote in my journal,
unread the books I stayed awake with,
unhike the trails I followed,
click back and back until
there is an empty search window
to fill.

       What would life be like
       without me?

@themoonforreal

Give me a good reason to exit this life early.

I can't think of one.

4. Mom's mac and cheese, Dad's tortilla soup, my sister's sandwich experiments.

5. Spadefoot toads calling from the wash after the monsoon.

6. Getting freaked out by running into a gang of javelinas snorting down the trail.

Rite of Passage

Give me a carved mask to wear while I dance,

> give me embers to stare into,

> > give me a sweat lodge to enter,

> > > give me an all-night feast,

> > give me a wooden tower to leap from

> > with my ankles bound in vines,

> give me a brand on the back,

singeing my skin,

give me a row of cattle to hurdle over,

> > give me wasp nests to bash with my

> bare hands,

> > > give me bulls to run with,

> > give me an animal to track alone by

moonlight,

give me a song I can't stop singing.

@themoonforreal
People don't look to me the way they used to.
That's why I like you. You want me to wink and
explain everything.

Speedway Between Gates Pass and Old Tucson, 6:52 PM

Shadows consume ocotillo, cholla,
and barrel cactus.
We rush to make it to the giant rock
in the desert,
follow the trail
through the arroyo
with a root sticking out
I always
mistake for a snake.

We hike the trail
until we spot the
15-foot-high square rock
which appears insurmountable from the front
but behind it
the rock is shattered
and you can
climb the pieces
to reach the top.

The sun glares
above the rawboned mountains
ready to leap

over the horizon.
We sit on the boulder's flat surface.
Matas smokes a cigarette,
I turn away from the sun
toward the rock walls
and the road snaking back
into the city.
The thin breeze
blows through gaps
in the mountains' teeth,
the sun
prepares
to dive over the peaks.

Hasty wind fumbles
through the arm holes
of our shirts.
Clouds stretched thin
across the sky
light up
sherbet orange.
As the sun
sinks,
the orange darkens to
red,
two birds

skip across the sky.
"Why'd she do it?" I ask,
breaking the calm of the desert.
Matas shrugs,
Sci-fi spits off the rock,
neither offers an explanation.

@themoonforreal
Why are you kids killing yourself? Follow me to the
other side of the globe and I'll show you suffering.

7. Movie previews in the theater with candy snuck in from Walgreens, sipping soda through a Red Vine licorice straw.

8. Singing song lyrics into a fan on a hot day.

9. Stumbling out of a matinee movie in the summer and the first blast of hot air after freezing for 2 hours inside.

I pull back the heavy church door,
photographs of J.
line the wall,
last year's prom picture
posed in front of plastic philodendrons
and Styrofoam Greek columns,
J. in a purple tutu
pudgy and barely old enough to walk,
candid shots of her,
arms flung around camp friends
all in tie-dye shirts they made.

> *Yvonne stops in front of me,*
> *and leans towards a photo,*
> *mascara clumped on her lashes,*

> *"That's my dress."*

Her saying it
makes it real,
as if J. wearing Yvonne's summer dress means
it could have been Yvonne,
or any of us,
that maybe these
bodies are outfits
all going out of style.

@themoonforreal
More people come and go than you'll ever know.
Still it's a shame about J.

Big Square Rock by Gates Pass, 7:26 PM

Silence congeals
after sunset.
Thicker than the normal quiet
of the Sonoran Desert,
the landscape
sucks in its breath
to observe a moment of silence
for the passing sun.
For a few minutes
no lizards scuttle under volcanic rocks,
no grackles call,
the wind caught in an inhale.
The desert
sits silent.
We wait
with ancient rock
until the desert moves again,
right on cue.

@themoonforreal

Anyone can die…it's harder to live.

Why are you upset?

10. Eavesdropping on people blabbering away on their cell phone in bathroom stalls.

11. Bands storming back on stage for an encore of my favorite song.

12. Singing old songs in the car, karaoke style.

Her father stands behind the
pulpit in his navy blue suit.

"Thank you
for coming."

His face sunken,
as if addressing us
from the coral floor
of a murky sea.
Don't understand
how he's able to do it,
but he tells stories about J.,
while the audience
wipes their eyes.

At the end
he says,
"If you
want to know how
J. died,
you can
find me
after the service
and I'll tell you."

We want to know,
but we don't want to know.

@themoonforreal
I was there when she died. What do you want to
know? She was dead before she fell off the rock.

The Dirt Trail Through the Arroyo, 7:32 PM

Before dark,
we climb off the rock
and weave our way
back towards the car.
I slide down into the arroyo
and stop.
A snake
lies across the path.
Squinting in dusk light
I notice it's the root
and curse myself
for fearing
the same thing
over and over again
when it's not real
to begin with.

We pile in the car,
the doors slamming
echoes in the valley.
I start the car
but wait
to turn the music on.
The quiet sunset still
rings in my head.

@themoonforreal
You liked her…didn't you? Why didn't you tell her
when you could?

13. Sliding down golf course hills on blocks of ice we bought from Circle K.

14. Driving around with the windows rolled down until the city cools off.

15. Out on a night walk and discovering an art gallery opening with free food and good art.

After the funeral,
her boyfriend, Aiden,
comes over to us.
His clothes wrinkled
and disheveled,
he's missed a spot, shaving,
under his nostrils.

He tells us
she tried to take pills
and it didn't work
so
she shot
herself.

She wanted
to make sure.

@themoonforreal
No point in taking your life, Envo. You haven't
lived yet.

East of Gates Pass, 7:43 PM

Driving back up the hill,
Tucson spread out before us,
its lights glistening, winking.
From this far away
the city appears full of action.

At last the moon returns over the horizon
and I can confess to her all the thoughts
too difficult to say
to anyone else.

I've known J. since 7th grade
but 6 facts in particular
stand out:

1.) When she hugged me she'd lift me off the
ground although I'm twice her size. Big
earthy-hugs that envelop you like the warm
flour smell of stepping into a tortilla factory.

2.) She was beautiful in a forest nymph kind
of way—5'3", toothy smile, bouncy, good
solid laugh. Her short hair pushed behind
her temples which often looked shiny.

3.) She ate oversized oranges and bit into the bitter skin to start peeling them.

4.) She loved to dance.

5.) She volunteered with AIDS patients and had friends who were dying for real.

6.) She owned an orange tabby cat named Miles who trailed her when she strolled around the block, not on a leash or anything. Miles showed up on her porch without tags and she adopted him.

Miles followed her everywhere.
Slept on her legs on top of the blanket,
gazed at her when she slurped bowls
of Rice Krispies
and dug her nails into pomegranates.
When she drove off to school,
he watched her car leave from the front window
and meowed.

What's Miles
doing now?

Not like J.'s parents
could explain her death
to the cat.
No one could
explain it to me.

Do her parents still
let the cat sleep
in her room?

What about
the front
window?

Is Miles
still
waiting?

@themoonforreal

She's dead, not you. Go and do something.

16. Arriving at the last page of a book that changed the way I view the world, and that quiet moment after reading the last sentence and shutting the book.

17. Waking up in the morning unsure of where I am because my dream feels so real, I'm still half inside it.

18. The smell of fresh paint, wet gardens, suntan lotion, fresh baked bread and brewing coffee.

Does J. Remembers These 6 Facts About Me?

1.) I'm taking classes at Pima Community College next year because I don't know what I want to study and why spend a bunch of money in Flagstaff at NAU trying to figure out what interests me. My Dad works for Pima but I won't run into him because he teaches online Psychology courses.

2.) People think I resemble David Duchovny; more than one person told me—which is weird. He's this old actor and he doesn't look like me anyway. I'm sure no one goes up to him and says, "Hey, are you Enzo Jones' dad?" He'd say, "Who's Enzo?"

3.) I live in a neighborhood known for its trailer park where a meth lab got busted. Walking by the meth trailer for months, I didn't notice anything but dirty chickens pecking at their cinder block steps.

4.) Every day I wear a black t-shirt, baggy shorts, and flip flops unless it's winter when I wear jeans.

5.) My favorite food is Los Betos bean burritos with extra guacamole and a large horchata (easy ice) from the drive-through Betos at Dodge and Alvernon because they make it better.

6.) J. and I danced once, at an all ages club downtown with walls covered in graffiti and these break dance guys who wore gas masks. Not sure why they wore masks. Maybe to keep out the smoke machine stench and sweat in the summer air.

Everyone circled around the gas mask guys doing windmills.

J. and I danced under the strobe light, her white teeth illuminated in rapid bursts.

The light too fast to see clearly, the music too loud for us to hear each other.

She grabbed my hand and we slow danced, as a joke, I think.

The crowd around the break dancers
hollered about a crazy move,
and she held onto me.

@themoonforreal

You'll never know if she would've loved you.
That story is over. Find another.

Secluded in the Men's Hut

I read in certain tribes
the boys are secluded for years.
They believed the longer guys
were isolated,
the stronger they'd be
when they came out.
What if I were (purposefully)
secluded in high school?
What if study hall is the men's hut
of our tribe.

        Our teacher, Mr. Ortiz,
        throws his paper down.

        "The girls need
        to leave the room."

        He races to the door
        and locks the guys inside.

        "You can't leave here until
        you understand
        what it means to be a man."

The guys in study hall are already

talking about sex
and he jumps into the conversation
and sets them straight.
He pulls me into the group
and we speak in hushed voices
about lives taken, animals hunted,
tales of the old ones…older than upper classmen.

Perhaps, after several years,
we'll leave at dawn on the last day of school
and find an animal
(it'd help if the school mascot was a living creature
and not a Ranger, whatever that means).
We'll find a wild animal, like a bull,
loose on the soccer field,
sacrifice it with weapons we fashion
from our broken desks,
and carry the meat to the school elders.
We march to their classrooms
and hand them dripping slabs
of flesh as they arrive to teach.
To Mr. Ortiz, who stayed with us
through years of seclusion,
we'll give the bull's thick heart;
to the principal, the slippery liver,
and each of his secretaries

receives a warm glass of blood
so they also experience the taste of the hunt.
And every elder in the school,
whether lunch lady, hall monitor, teacher,
or guidance counselor,
will taste the meat
and give us benediction
for a long and fruitful life.

@themoonforreal

When people landed on me, I thought life would change, but they just left footprints and flew off.

19. Eye contact with a complete stranger and harboring a secret bond.

20. Kissing ………. in the upstairs drama prop room, on the couch, hidden behind broken music stands.

21. When horses spot me when I'm out walking and they trot towards me as if we're old friends reuniting.

Roadside Markers & Thoughts to Myself

Driving towards Tucson,
nervous clouds stampede across the sky.

Here's how I play good student.

Coyotes trot
through creosote bushes,
pink tongues dangle
from their jagged lips,
soft sand
cool on their paws.
How many sticky nights
of hunting
in dust?

Here's how I rush out knowing
nothing.

Crosses covered in silver tinsel
on the roadside,
mark the exact spots where people died.
Identify the location
where a Harley crashed
headlong into a telephone pole,

47

where drunk drivers
crushed bicycles,
or where pickup trucks
rattled off the road.

> Here's everything I've memorized,
> why don't I know anything?

The city lights
loom before us,
rotten mattresses left out
in the rain,
plastic bags snagged on
chain link fences.

> Here are the tests I've taken.
> Why am I thrown off by the real
> tests of my life?

The ice cream truck drives
so slow
you think
it's a drive by.

> Here's my report card,
> do I understand anything yet?

@themoonforreal
I can't console you right now,
I'm busy with the tides.

I've Known These Guys Since Kindergarten

Sci-fi talks
a big game and quotes
every movie ever made,
but I've dropped him off
and heard his dad and step-mom
scream at each other
as we pulled
up in front of their "southwestern villa."
They're the only people on the planet who call him
Sebastiano
and not by his nickname, Sci-fi.
He picks up
lots of girls,
but no matter how hard he tries,
he can't pick
a new step-mom.

Matas reads books
I don't understand
with titles like:
*The Origin of Consciousness in the Breakdown of
the Bicameral Mind.*
But when he's finished
his abstract oil paintings and logged off

his online chess games,
he's alone.
All his intelligence can't change
the fact his father
has a new family
on the other side
of town.

@themoonforreal
The people crossing the border need me tonight...
don't waste my time.

22. Slurping Icees under fireworks, while a band plays louder than they're supposed to.

23. Lost in a strange neighborhood and finding a family reunion under poorly strung Christmas lights. Everyone feasts off of paper plates and they invite me in to eat with them.

24. Dramatic air guitar solos to cheesy metal songs.

Between the Landscape & My Head

Clink of metal bats
on the baseball diamond,
red-faced kids
with sunburnt necks
climb backstops.

Here's me needing to graduate
from high school.

Streetlights hang their heads
over hot pavement
depressed by
their meager light.

Here's me talking to the guidance
counselor about next year—
I place no faith in aptitude tests.

Homeless guys pace the median
and peer into car windows
as if looking for long lost
family members.

Here's me waiting for the last bell
of high school to ring. The last
time I'll base my life around a
musical chime.

Moths frantic at street lights;
bats nose-deep in cactus fruit;
quail in the cool grass
follow each other,
snooty and proper.

I spent the last four years trying
to figure out how to escape high
school and find something—anything—that makes sense.

@themoonforreal
Don't blame me…I'm not the one who makes you
people crazy.

We Don't Talk About the Funeral, How Her Family is Coping, Or Her Boyfriend, Aiden

"What do you call the
   mouse shadow on the
   second moon?" Sci-fi
   says, quoting Dune, David
   Lynch's version.

Matas leans over
and pushes the car lighter.
Under the streetlight his hair
shines
with flecks of grey in it—
even though he's 17.

"Shut up with the quotes!"

"We call that one Muad'
   Dib," Sci-fi continues,
   lowering his voice,
   "Could I be known as Paul
   Muad'Dib?"

"What are we doing tonight?"

"There's a party at Speedway
& Main," Sci-fi says.

"Like the 7th & Cherry
party last night?" Matas
asks.

> "There's always a
> party at 7th & Cherry."

Which is usually true.
But yesterday we drove around
looking for a non-existing party.

> Sci-fi pushes his hands
> through his shaggy hair.

> "Speedway & Main, for
> real—a band's playing. Tons
> of girls are gonna be there."

"I can't stay out too late,
I have a paper to write by Monday."

> Matas pulls out the glowing
> car lighter, touches it to the end

of his American Spirit.

"For Parks?
That was assigned three
weeks ago.
What have you been doing?"

I sigh and scan the radio—

"Even I wrote my paper,"
 Sci-fi says,
"Which topic did you pick?"

"Rites of passage."

Matas exhales
out the window.

"I wondered
 who'd be stupid enough
 to pick that one."

@themoonforreal
Call me the next time there's a good party.
It's boring in the sky.

25. Full moon drives in the desert when the perfect song comes on as if the DJ snatched it from my head.

26. Walking along the Rillito River on the few days a year the wash flows and the parks are full of large family gatherings with piñatas and music blasting through crappy speakers.

27. Climbing to the top of the giant A on A Mountain and swapping ghost stories about Bloody Mary and pretending to hear La Llorona cry for her children.

People Watching

Eyes covered in rimless glasses
and eyes with prison tattoo tear drops
at their corners.
Eyes that glare, not letting in any sight,
and eyes which take it all in too much
and dart from faces to menus mounted
on restaurant windows.
Eyes seeking me a silent brotherhood,
and eyes which never catch my own.
Eyes which try and name me,
watch my clothes, the posture of my head.
Everything carried in their eyes,
droopy, squinted, glancing sidelong,
blinking Morse code SOS,
flashing with laughter, dim with sadness,
the whites of their eyes bottoming out.

The homeless woman pleads and gutter punks beg,
and all of us politely ignore each other,
with long stares hanging in the air.
We pass each other, headed home to sleep
in different parts of town, or in the park,
the back of abandoned cars, or on roofs.
From each corner of the city we pass each other,

watching.

All the eyes, the library of them,
filled to the brim with stories they'll never utter
to a single soul,
shelved within themselves,
unopened to everyone who passes.

@themoonforreal
Not my first rodeo. I wish it was though.
For this to feel new again.

There should be a pause—
where traffic pulls to the roadside,
and the flag stands motionless,
not rippling in the breeze.
The people on the street stop,
and power down their phones.

We take a deep breath,
look around at the frozen world,
and exhale,
knowing we paused for you, if only for a moment.
But the world doesn't stop spinning,
for any of us.
We still talk about
last weekend's parties.
People drive along the street,
listening to FM 93.7,
as though nothing has happened.

@themoonforreal
How many full moons will you have in this life?
There's not an endless supply.

28. The perfect desert party with a blazing bonfire and lots of old friends.

29. Jumping off waterfalls into murky water at Redington Pass on senior ditch day.

30. Riding my bike at Saguaro National Park in the morning and dodging rattlesnakes sunning on the road.

31. Exploring the U of A lawn and running into groups of people playing weird games or practicing dance routines or handing out information for super random causes.

Here's Me Again, Driving the Streets

We speed by
hourly motels,
graveyards too long
to hold your breath past,
railroad tracks
hand sewn into the city's
Frankenstein face.

Here's me not understanding
what people say. Is it a different
language which you can't
translate until you're over 19?

The smell of a tortilla factory
wafts in through the open windows.
Piñatas dangle outside the corner market,
their bright paper skins
sway in the night breeze.
A boy out front
licks a saladito
lodged in a half lemon.

Here's me needing to get my life
together.

The flirtatious street lights
wink me on,
green eyed and encouraging.
The town half-covered
in dust,
all of us second-hand objects
in an antique shop—
untouched and outdated.

> Here's me needing to change for
> good.

A public pool
diving board
rattles with
backflips and cannon balls,
the smell of coconut sunscreen
alive in the air,

the street's June bug buzz
that tonight something—anything—
might happen.

@themoonforreal
Wasting your life, wondering
if you're wasting your life.

4th Avenue, 8:24 PM

Pow-wow cries
    from a gymnasium
        pour out,

high pitched
    wails run into the street
        and climb stars
        bare-fisted.

        "I played this Russian guy
        in chess club," Matas says, "who
        everyone
        was scared to play. Just because
        he's Russian doesn't mean
        he's a good player.
        He didn't know
        the King's Gambit opening."

        Sci-fi and I glance out the
        windows at 4th Avenue, not
        following Matas's story.

Crusty gutter punks
    coo over their malnourished dogs,

shaky hands outstretched
to bum leftover
Styrofoam food containers
of eggplant parmesan.

Brittle tumbleweeds lodge against
sewer grates.
Not rolling anywhere but into pieces.

High school girls outside of Dairy Queen
with their Dilly Bars
dripping
on warm cement benches.
Unaware of the cars
that roll by them,
and taste every lick.

"I debated between opening with
either the Gunderam Defense or
the St. George's Defense because,
statistically, they're both good
openings if you're white," Matas
says, recounting his chess match.

We float by Epic Café.

Day old bread cuddles on
            the café counter,

hot hiss of
            lattes,

fliers pinned on
            the wall with thumb tacks.

Old guys with ZZ Top beards
            play weathered chessboards,

puff filterless
            cigarettes,

pick tobacco
            pieces from the tips
            of their educated tongues.

People marooned
            in front of their
            laptops.

Staring into their
        screens

as if they
were port windows
and they were searching
for land.

"I thought of the Latvian Gambit;
I mean, why not?" Matas laughs,
"Long story short, it was check-
mate in 12 moves."

@themoonforreal
I know what's inside of you. You don't tell the others.

32. The one day when it snowed in Tucson and people stared at the sky as if witnessing a Christmas miracle, though it wasn't Christmas, and everyone wandered the streets dumbstruck, trying to scrape together enough snow to make anorexic snowmen.

33. Buying taro root boba tea at Miss Saigon, and my drink's filled with the perfect amount of tapioca pearls.

34. Out on a family walk with my parents, sister and our two dogs in the wash. The dogs bolt off cheetah fast through the sand and we tell stories as the dogs run wild, and Dad keeps interrupting the conversation to yell, "Lionel! Moe!" so the dogs don't sprint off forever.

35. The second round of eating on Thanksgiving when I hurry back for the best dishes, and realizing I'll savor these leftovers for days.

Mailmen, Sketchy House at Speedway & Main

Matas and Sci-fi go out back
to search for the keg.
I slump down in the living room
with a bunch of varsity football players.
They stole a pile of mailboxes
from up the street
and pass them around
like a ritual drug.
Levi Harris grips a silver mailbox
at both ends
and rams it straight into his
sweaty forehead,
the mailbox dents in
and he laughs.
Levi passes the mailbox to Tyler Young
who slams it into his head
as hard as he can,
he pulls the mailbox back from his forehead and
a trickle of blood drips down his face,
he smiles and burps Miller Lite.
Tyler passes the mailbox
to me.
A bright blood mark glistens
on the outside of the broken box,

I flip it around and check inside.

A stack of junk mail,

jostles around

but I don't open

any letters

because that would be

a federal offense.

@themoonforreal
No need to get angry at the football players for calling her "the dead girl." She is dead.

Waiting to Speak

I listen to what people blabber on about,
their straight teeth purple with wine,
their sweat ripe with cheap beer,
their eyes red with weed.
Everyone's laughing,
not because of anything funny,
but because we're unsure of what else to do,
we huddle in mutual jokes—pretend everything's fine.

I'm waiting
to enter the conversation,
but what to say and to whom?
Could I say to my friends:
"We're going to die—one of us already gone—and
we're headed our separate ways and nothing will be
the same and I'm both happy and sad about leaving
and sometimes I'm so unsatisfied I might burst and
no offense to you or this city but it's all unfunny
and uninteresting. And if these are the best days of
my life—I'm screwed.

Can you tell me
what the point is
to all of this?"

@themoonforreal
I'm watching everything and never part of it.
Just like you.

36. Spotting coyotes running through midnight parking lots as if wild animals are taking over the city.

37. Strolling through the butterfly garden at Brandi Fenton Park and remembering the kids who never lived to be as old as I am now.

38. Laying back in those weird laser light shows chairs.

39. The long drive back from a concert at the fairgrounds with my ears ringing in the darkness before Tucson.

Taken, 9:17 PM

Sci-fi chats up a foothills girl
with red hair and a flirty face.
Matas scrolls through pictures on
Yvonne's phone they took two minutes before.
I picture J.'s face
after she's danced,
her temples dark with sweat,
her skin shiny.
She smiles—not her strained smile
stuck in her mouth
like a bite of microwaved food not cooked through,
but her smile which flashes
from her eyes,
a personal monsoon
sneaking over from the east-side.

I envision a black sack
thrown over my head
right in the middle of the mediocre party.
But like with everything else,
no one in the room notices.
Men call out
as they carry me on their shoulders
out the broken door

into the night air.

The musty cloth
chafes against my nose.

"I need to tell Matas and Sci-fi
where I'm going so
they can find another ride."

A tribesman slaps me
across the head
as if my words are
throwing off the rhythm
of their footsteps.

"Get your hands off me," the other
boys shout,
dragged from their bedrooms,
snatched from the hazy glow
of their computer screens and
virtual lives.

"I'm on my last guy,
I need to get back to my game."

The men's heavy feet stomp in unison.
I cannot see through the cloth
where we're going
the muffled cries of other boys,
surround me,
frightened for their lives.
The sound of Saturday night traffic dies out.
We're fixed on their shoulders,
not sure what waits for us.

A fire warms my skin,
its crackles and tiny pops
mix with the chanting voices.
They yank the hood from my head
and I inhale a mouthful of smoke.
Forced towards the bright bonfire,
my clothes are cut from me,
thrown into the blaze.

I'm dressed in freshly killed animal skins,
my face streaked with mud,
beads of bone hung on my neck.
Across the rising sparks,
tears fall from the boys' faces
painted like animals.

The chant rings in my ears,
feet pound the sand,
I clap my hands,
despite myself.
I turn with the dancers around the fire.

The drummers wailing, pounding,
calling out.
Dust and smoke surround us,
embers flee into the sky
until they disappear.

The boys torn from their rooms
now fix their eyes on the flames.
There's no crying about what's lost.

We burn under the fire,
under the song,
under the moon,
and we won't stop
for three days straight.

@themoonforreal
Peeking over the mountain big and low on the
horizon is the best. Like everyone else,
I want to be seen.

I'm So Angry, I May Start a Blog

The punk band blares in the backyard
by the keg and the shiny red plastic cups.
We slam against the chain link fence,
in the gravel lot,
cars parked helter-skelter,
headlights cut through dust.
Everyone bounces around the band,
screams at the moon,
raises their drinks to the police helicopter
circling overhead shining its spotlight down on us.

Tires screech as they pull out to race nowhere,
shouting at the helicopter in the sky
as if to Greek gods
pestering our weekend plans.
The cops will arrive soon, with serious mustaches,
lights flashing, checking IDs.

If we could, we'd destroy this city,
shred its strip-malls to pieces,
pull out the palm trees lining the streets,
and throw the paintings of coyotes
wearing handkerchiefs around their necks
like confetti against the perfect sunsets.

We'd rage forever, burn ourselves
into white-hot oblivion.
Even though we grit our teeth
and howled,
the piñata moon
just hung there
waiting to break.

@themoonforreal
I'm not a Ouija board. I cannot talk to the dead.
Make your own peace.

@themoonforreal
Not my fault you can't hear me. You believe I'm
mute, when I'm talking to you all the time.

@themoonforreal
You and I have a lot in common. We're both alone.

40. Noticing a girl in the halls, and knowing I'll be her boyfriend one day, and all those secret smiles between us until it happens.

41. After a big rain when the roads flood and no one's driving, taking an inner tube and floating down our street.

42. People flipping out at the Elm street house, making a pyramid of old couches you can sit on.

43. Hanging out on the big rock in the desert until it grows dark and a light rain falls. Coyotes yelp in the distance and I howl back to them.

What Message Do I Carry?

What I want to articulate is not a joke,
it presses against my rib cage,
a frozen mammoth stuck inside me
waiting to thaw.
It's something crucial,
something that needs to be shouted, along the lines
of "The British are coming!
The British are coming!"

But I can't identify the words I need to express.

We're not under attack,
though there's an unspoken urgent message
I carry through the night
in my parents' used Corolla,
backed up in my guts, a life sentence of constipation
or a 1,000 year pregnancy under skies
never breaking open with rain.

Each time I look for an opening
where I can break in and remark,
here's what I've waited
my whole life to say
and it must be said.

@themoonforreal
Why don't you fit in anywhere?

After the funeral,
we drive to
the top of A mountain.
Tucson looks
so sharply cut against the desert,
I turn away.
Like when you put on new glasses
and everything's too clear at first.

Three grey haired guys in trucker hats
fly remote control planes
from the mountain top,
their planes whoosh over hills
doing loops and turns,
hanging on the dry wind.

We watch the planes
until we forget we're watching them.
We gaze
at the hollow sky
and there might not be
any point
in ever speaking again.
Maybe we should buy gliders
and sit on the mountain,
which is actually a hill

with a big letter A on it,
and fly our planes.

@themoonforreal
I'm far older than people. But I'm not feeble.
Believe me when I say your problems are small…
even if they feel bigger than the sky.

44. Sitting around the campfire at Camp Cooper as a kid, sleeping in those freezing bunks, playing the camouflage animal game in the morning where you hide from the person pretending to be a predator.

45. Driving to Mount Lemmon, lying on hoods of cars and pointing out shooting stars.

46. Spending time with people in person where there are no hashtags or likes to dole out. The comments are in person and I know who my friends are.

47. The moment right before an exciting event, lights dimming at the theater before a movie I've waited for years begins; at a concert, people screaming in the dark as the band walks on stage; the second right before kissing someone for the first time.

Barrio Libre

Rainbow colored DJ lights flash from a quinceañera
at the Convention Center.
Guys outside lean against their polished cars.
The reflection of their rims
and their girlfriends' earrings
sparkle as I pass.
Candles flicker at El Tiradito Wishing Shrine,
metal nets rattle from miracle three pointers
at the park,
bottles smash against pavement,
TVs blare through open doorways of houses.
I stop in front of Carrillo
where I used to go to school,
which was once a lake, zoo, garden,
back when everyone carried buck knives.

Kids walk the tightrope curb barefoot.
Everyone out on the street,
standing by mango colored murals.
The big "A" of A Mountain, written in rocks,
the beginning of a sentence spelled out
in white washed stones.
A circular sentence wrapped around the valley,
stretched across the Catalinas,

plastered on the Rincons,

in small print on the Santa Ritas,

ending on the Tucson Mountains,

"A…boy…walks…into…the…old…pueblo…"

@themoonforreal
Are you waiting for a momentous sign?
The heavens part and the options are laid out?

Those Who Died Too Soon

All those who died too young
on Dead Man's Curve,
drunk at Redington Pass,
brain aneurism in their bedroom,
hit by semis while fixing a flat,
drowning in Sabino Canyon.

              All those who died too soon
              sit on the edges of the clouds
              and flick pennies
              at our heads,

          "Stop wasting time."

They follow us through
corner markets,
whisper in our ears to buy Jumex Mango Nectar,
a bag of limes,
coconut popsicles.
Those who died too soon,
jam requests in fortune cookies
and hope we'll receive their messages
to go watch their favorite band at the fairgrounds,
so they can hitch a ride

and scale the ten-foot-high speakers,
nod their heads along with the crowd.

"Wake up and watch the sun rise,"
they yell to us when the applause
dies down.
"Don't squander your life
waiting
for it
to begin."

@themoonforreal
Your life is not a movie. Stop waiting for the
slow-mo shot and the emo music and do something.

48. Green Jalisco hot sauce, blue corn tamales, guacamole (when the avocado is ripe), chips and salsa from Rosa's, eegee's, cheese crisps, roadside taco toppings across the border, Coke from a bottle on a Mexican beach, horchata with tiny crunchy ice, mocha floats from Bentley's, junior high mariachi bands, bonfires, parties to find, owls perched on top of light posts, coyotes out of sight in the distance, mesquite pods rattling, wind through saguaro thorns, 64 ounce drinks from Circle K, fire drills in the middle of class, four square games, and that weird game where you try and wrap a ball around a pole.

49. Public pools, school pools, backyard pools, rickety above ground pools, black bottom pools, infinity pools, deflating plastic blow-up pools and outdoor little ponds of water, constantly in water, forever trying to cool down.

50. The taste of kissing someone in the movie theater after they've eaten nachos with jalapeños.

51. Tossing throwing stars at boards as a kid and being both worried about getting caught and feeling like a total ninja.

Call to Adventure, Speedway & Campbell, 9:58 PM

Waiting at the stoplight, a tribe surrounds the Corolla.
Matas & Sci-fi mess with their phones
and don't notice the 12 warriors encircling us.
The chief gestures for me to come with them.
I roll the window down, "What will we eat?"
His cheeks puff in and out, he stares at me blankly.
"Okay, if you cut me, is the knife sterilized?"
The chief looks to his right-hand man.
Their faces tattooed, cuts still fresh on their skin,
notches taken from their ears.
"Sterilization," I say, "I don't want you to cut with
the same knife you use on everybody else.
You know, infection, disease."
They watch me from the street,
dead-faced and unblinking.
A truck passes and they reach
into the car to grab me.
"Stop…I need to pack supplies…first aid kit, signal
mirror, water proof Band-Aids."
As soon as "waterproof" slips out of my mouth,
they turn and jaywalk
across the intersection.
"Wait!" I jump out of the car,

"let me grab my
  antibacterial wipes and I'll be right with you,
  I want this."
  They shimmy over a wall and
  vanish from the blinking turn signals.

@themoonforreal
Not to be rude, but another aimless night of hunting
for parties, another shooting, another suicide.

Driving by Rincon H.S., 10:09 PM

1.

Straining to hear the sounds of my school,
as if the empty building is a shell
I cradle against my ear.

Sneakers squeaking on linoleum floors,
catchy cellphone rings, trunk speakers roaring
from the student parking lot,

steady panting of the incinerator at night—
who knows what they're burning—
sipping of burnt coffee in the teachers' lounge,
the principal schmoozing parents,

bell chimes between class,
flag rope clanging against the pole,

plastic letters on the marquee slid into place:
"Good luck JV volleyball,"
the quiet click of eyes
as they roll over each other.

2.

I've visited
every corner
of this town

but still
it feels like
the city is empty.

Not like a pocket,
or a money clip with
no bills,

not empty like the vacant eyes
of a brain starved zombie,

or a stomach
protruding
from
starvation
with the belly-button
popped out.

It's empty
exactly

the way it is,

not even metaphorical,

it's empty like
a desert city

built on a draining
aquifer.

@themoonforreal
You get drunk and it wears off, you fall in love and
quickly climb out of it.

52. Meerkats at Reid Park Zoo.

53. Hiding out in big-box stores to escape the
    heat and finding toiletries I need to buy.

54. People escaping from the sun in little slivers
    of shade at the bus top, behind telephone
    poles and scrawny mesquite trees.

55. Parking lot geometrical calculations—
    trying to gauge where the shade will fall by
    the time I leave.

My Gom Jabbar

1.

> Sci-fi quotes Dune, the
> movie of the night.
> "Put your right hand in the
> box."

> He pretends he's choked
> up, uses his whiny Luke
> Skywalker-you're-not-my
> father-voice.

> "What's in the box?"

> "Pain," Matas says,
> playing into his game.

He turns the music louder to drown out Sci-fi.
The speakers rattle the plastic dashboard,
cracked from the incessant sun.
The bass thumps up our spines.

2.

The unsaid words blare,
like a lowrider sneaking up behind me
at midnight.
Creeping over speed bumps to not bottom out.
The ragged boom, boom, boom from trunk speakers,
fuzzy and adamant,
a heartbeat forced on the neighborhood.
Coming up behind me, driving slow,
I don't know who's in the passenger seat.
If they'll lean out the window with a gun and say,
"Game over,"
squeeze the trigger and I'm finished.

3.

I float into the sky to meet J.
at the light at the end of the tunnel
and say, "How do you think your parents feel? Or
Aiden? Or any of us?
And not that we can weigh our grief against another's
but why did the Holocaust survivors go on living?
And the Lost Boys of the Sudan, who lost their
whole families
and watched friends dragged off by lions,

they carry on,
some of them with missing limbs.
And there you were with your body,
intact, beautiful, graceful by anyone's standards.
How could you do it?
Where was your strength
with which you argued
about the death penalty?
The courage it took to ask Aiden out
instead of waiting for him to come to you.
I'm not supposed to say it
because depression is a disease,
but don't we fight any disease we have?
Why wave the white flag and
let yourself be consumed?
What the hell were you thinking?"

I fall back to my body,
after I got the last word,
and live with a bullet scar dotting the "i" of a
"bored life" tattoo
I get inked across my stomach.

The lowrider rolls by,
the passengers nod their head with the music,
not noticing me,

not leaning out the window with guns,
but laughing with each other, smoking cigarettes,
probably searching for a party.

@themoonforreal
You won't get shot with a magic bullet
which explains everything.

Bide One's Time

We pace washes with La Llorona.

We roam cattle yards
with blood-thirsty chupacabras.

We orbit blindly
as crows weigh down
the chinaberry trees.

Always we are waiting,
on picnic benches,
on stoops, in post office lines,

waiting by stairs
for friends to drive up,

for laundry to finish,

for concert tickets,

for the rain to come,

for our eyes to carry
monsoons,

for a flock of words
to rise from our throats

and beat their wings against the startled air.

@themoonforreal
What do you want to do with your life now?
Not tomorrow.

56. Sliding down hills on red fast food trays.

57. Brooklyn Pizza after school.

58. Dust devils and haboobs gusting into town.

59. Finding lonely shopping carts in the middle of nowhere and riding them around.

What Isn't Here, 10:35 PM

We're above ground, cruising around,
searching for parties we can't find,
she's underground,
in a closed casket,
wearing a formal dress
she wouldn't be caught dead in
(if she were still alive).

I turn the music down,
"Are you satisfied?"

                    "You talking to me, Oprah?"
                    Sci-fi asks.

"Both of you," I say,
 realizing it's a dumb question
 to ask in the first place.
"Forget it."

                    "I'm satisfied with
                     two more weeks of high school,"
                    Matas says, knowing he's going
                    to Berkeley next year.

Sci-fi sticks his head out the
window and howls
louder than a drunk coyote.
He leans forward between
the front seats,
"I'm satisfied with the
number of that hot redhead
in my phone."

@themoonforreal
Even I tire of the repetition,
but there are new sights to see.

Hitchhiking Ghosts

The dead are out tonight, thumbing rides,
trying to figure out where to part their hair.
Still looking for last year's desert party,
they died before reaching.
They push phantom fingers into cellphones
and, getting no response, they search
the coin return slot of the last bus station pay phone.

Those who died too soon
hitchhike the last breeze of sunset,
ride the wind like bull riders
to the statue of Pancho Villa downtown and wait.
Looking for a cigarette to bum,
a revolution to start, a warehouse to burn,
and seeing none,
they catch a breeze
to find us,
to ride on our dented car roof
as we drive in circles.
They dangle their heads down
through our open windows
curious where we're going
wasting so much gas.
The dead become bored of us,

drift out into the desert
to sit on rocks and
watch the night pass,
swapping stories about the good old days
when they breathed the same air we do.

@themoonforreal
When I was young, no one wanted to die.
They'd stay awake watching me
because there were no TVs.

60. Struggling with chop sticks at Sushi Ten until I say screw it and eat with my hands.

61. Entering the kitchen as Dad pulls baked goods straight from the oven, bread, cookies, pie, whatever…. Knowing when it cools off I'm devouring the first bite.

62. Sabino Canyon, Ventana Canyon trail, end of Speedway east trail, end of Alvernon, Madera Canyon, Catalina State Park and of course Tumamoc Hill.

63. A good conversation with a friend where you actually listen to each other.

Sabino Canyon, 10:43 PM

We leave my car in the parking lot
and wander down the road
that shuttles tourists through the canyon
on trams during the day.

Heading out under the desert sky,
our faces to the wind,
night birds and crickets in the air,
the saguaros blooming under a clear-eyed moon.

Moonlight drenches the canyon,
coyotes yelp to each other,
lope through the desert
on a hunt we cannot take part in.

The further we hike,
the higher the canyon walls tower over us.
Though it's dark we sweat,
because the sun still clings to the pavement.
We watch the silhouettes of cactus,
the outline of the mountains.
An owl turns its head around as we pass.

The longer we hike
the less we talk.
The city lights gone behind us,
stars creep out
like frightened animals
becoming curious,
peeking through
the dark sky.

@themoonforreal
I too wonder what the world would be like without me.
But you and I cannot run away.

Speaking Ill of the Dead

They say not to speak ill of the dead
but you didn't live long enough
for me to speak ill of you
while above ground
and when you were alive
I had nothing I wanted
to say against you.
How to pretend suicide makes sense?
That I say, well, it's her life,
she can do what she wants.
How can I say anything other than her actions are
stupid, selfish and wrong.

What can I tell the school counselor
about how I'm feeling?
If I cried, my tears would be coated
in white hot fury,
and if I laughed,
it'd cut the smile from your face.

Don't want to curse or praise you,
I want to understand what you did
and I never will.
You left us with questions

we can't answer
midway through a conversation
impossible to finish now.

@themoonforreal
More reasons to live than to die. Even if it doesn't
feel like it.

64. Huddled around a fire on Mount Lemmon, burning marshmallows, gazing up through pine trees.

65. Roaming around alone at night, listening to trains pass, finding hidden cafes where everyone's busy composing the next great American novel.

66. The clean taste of someone's skin after they've stepped out of the shower.

67. Amazing bites of nachos with the perfect cheese jalapeno ratio……. crisp apples, cold water, ice cream softened in the sun.

The last time we hung out,
me, Matas, and J. drove to Himmel Park at night.
The park with the rusted train engine
stranded in the middle
without tracks to roll forward on
and the solemn tennis courts,
nets catching the breeze
after park curfew.

Strolling past the dangerously
steep slide at the playground,
J. talks about dancing.

"Sometimes I can dance beyond
the edge of my body."

The sprinklers turn on and J. kicks her shoes off,
runs past the dented trash cans,
out into a soccer field—
arms outstretched—laughing.
Her short hair pushed behind her ears
with sprinkler water and sweat.
She leaps into the air—
Reenacting part of a routine she's choreographed.
The sprinklers click 360 degrees,
she spins in circles in the opposite direction

kicking her leg around,
a pirouette.
The water drenches her
and she spins,
mud forms around her bare feet.

Why didn't I recognize how depressed she was?
What if I could've stopped her?

J. stops laughing,
she's somewhere
inside herself,
spinning,
letting the outside
world blur.
The water hits her,
each time it passes
her pirouettes
quicken.
Her eyes fixed on
a point in
the distance,
she watches to keep
her balance.
It's not a crooked olive tree
or a cement picnic table

or the swings.
Perhaps her eyes
are fixed on
death.

@themoonforreal
It's just a phase they say of me.
But, it's true. Don't give up.

Desert Creek, 11:20 PM

Water trickles beyond the road,
cottonwood trees rise from the ravine
amongst cactus.
A little breath of life winds down the mountains.

The terrain jagged and we are soft,
softer than we think we are.
We don't understand the sacrifices
the desert makes to survive,
to let part of your body die
so the rest goes on living.
What do we understand of sacrifice?
What do we know of giving one's self completely
to keep on living?

The silence sinks on the canyon, settles on the ground.

Wrapped in the questions we carried:
Why'd she kill herself? Why are we still living?
What are we alive for anyway?
Wanting to remove these questions like homemade
tattoos on our necks
saying IGNORANT LOSER HERE in black ink.
We want to molt into adulthood and never look back,

shed the years of drippy snow cones,
birthday party wishes, and folded notes to girls
reading, "Will you go out with me, yes, no, maybe,
check box."

We walk to a pool of water at the roadside
and leave our clothes in the sand.

I wade into the creek,
a constellation of goose bumps race up my legs,
skin slips into dark liquid,
air blows along the water's surface.
The moon overhead makes us nothing more
than silhouettes.

Leaving behind everything.
Leave first meeting you in 7th grade
in a white t-shirt and pink shorts,
your hair longer then,
pulled back in a fluorescent scrunchie.
I leave the years of parties we both attended
from ice cream socials in the Carrillo cafeteria
to desert parties we needed 4-wheel drive to find.
I leave the small talk we mumbled to each other
on the phone
and all your dance recitals I sat through.

Pulling my arms through cool water, stars warble on
the surface,
the desert quiet except for the gentle rippling of the
creek.
I glide forward into the canyon,
as if swimming through dark sky,
floating through the dim years which led me here.

The desert owl calls,
the padded feet of coyotes scamper through brush,
horses at distant ranches snort,
and stomp their hooves in the sand.

In the desert pool, swimming, the night grows larger
around us.

I listen to lyrics on the radio but none of them say
what I'm feeling,
not in any of the books in my room,
nor any of the poems my English class forced me to
read.

I've heard mariachi bands pluck guitars
in packed restaurants in the rain,
I've heard concerts under washed-out stars,

and rattlesnakes shake their coiled tails,
and beautiful girls laugh to themselves
under their breath,
and every kind of instrument they'll play on the
radio,
and the endless squawk of voices
at my school in the halls between classes, but still,
none of it is what I need to hear.

Swimming in the water,
brisk against my skin.
I want to shout though it's too quiet to shout,
and I want to splash and yell and twist underwater
but it wouldn't take me out of this place inside.

All the dirt trails we followed,
all the midnight hash browns at Village Inn,
all the gallons of horchata we sipped
from Styrofoam cups,
all the phone numbers we swapped,
all the YouTube videos we've watched,
all the miles we drove around this city with the
odometer spinning,
all the times we said, "What should we do tonight?"

Why this high school,

why these friends,
these clothes,
these eyes,
this skin,
why this life
and not another?

@themoonforreal
Let's both go to sleep. There are only so many
dreams we can handle while awake.

68. An afternoon nap during a rainstorm and waking up refreshed.

69. Little kids explaining movie plots…that they're super excited about but it makes no sense.

70. Rodeo Vacation.

71. Winterhaven Christmas lights at dusk when the streets aren't crowded yet, and I sip hot chocolate and stroll along without a care in the world.

Here's my Paper

The paper I need to write
for Mr. Parks
makes me want to storm into his classroom
followed by a tribe,
our legs covered in shells,
rattle with each step.
We dance in barefoot,
"How can you tell me to write
about rites of passage?"
I call out,
and the dancers stomp
on the worn-out linoleum floor.
Mr. Parks cannot understand what I'm saying,
he tilts his head to one side like a confused dog,
I march towards him
and toss the report on his desk,
"Here's my paper."
The female dancers hop towards us,
beads jingle, shells clack together in their hair,
rocking from side to side,
and the male dancers leap onto his desk.
He tries to grab
my paper before their naked feet
pound it to pieces.

They crowd his desk and slap their legs
as they dance,
"How to live as a man in a world full of boys?"
I yell and the dancers repeat with me,
the drummers from the tribe enter the room,
heads thrown back in unrestrained song,
the metal rings on their decorated djembes
rattle as they stomp in,
they crowd the aisles of desks
and the other students glance around
unsure if they should stand up and dance
or flee.

Mr. Parks stands up.

"Get out!"

but he's drowned out by the drums
and the dancing, and the all-out singing,
and my words become shredded
under the thick calloused feet of the youngest dancer,
scars carved across his chest,
cuts he kept open
by continuing to bathe
so the wounds

swelled up.

Exactly as we came in,

we dance out of the room

leaving pieces of shell and footprints

along the ground

and the scraps of my paper

scatter across the floor.

@themoonforreal
The rain is coming to clean out the city. Go home.

Time to Put Away Childish Things

I swim away from Matas & Sci-fi
and stroll into the desert in only my skin.

A river of air covers me, and stops, as if reflective.
The scent of far off sunrise drifts towards us,
the blue before dawn, heads our way.
My anger carried off
in the breeze,
another tumbleweed to roll.

We walk out of our childhoods,
not the way a metal band struts out
of a stadium of screaming fans,
not the way a losing team staggers into the locker
room
at the end of the NBA finals,
towels draped over their heads, staring at the floor.

I head out of childhood the same way I walked into it,
barefoot, blindly exploring the ground before me.
The ssshh of sand as I step,
pebbles and goat's head thorns catch my feet,
as I search for a place to stand.

We're not dead, we're not alive,
we're in high school
watching the horizon
for smoke signals
about who to text.
We're stepping out of childhood,
our gobstopper eyes changing color.

I wrote my college entrance essay
about my goals,
though none of it's true,
it sounds good
but I've no idea what my goals are,
other than I need to
grow up.

Where's the voice inside me
that flattens
the city
like crop circles
in corn?
Where's
the voice
within me
rushing out?
A cool breeze

speaking
with absolute
certainty—
that the
drought
of this life
is
over.

@themoonforreal
Life is not over, only high school. Drive home and
I'll talk to you tomorrow.

72. Purring cats on my lap, first tap of fat rain on skylight panels, Mom laughing with her best friends on the phone.

73. Waking up in the middle of the night to go pee outside and watching the moon, everyone in the neighborhood asleep, as the sky lightens.

74. An all-night rave at the airplane graveyard.

75. Parents carrying their sleeping children back to the car on the 4th of July.

I never told anyone,
but the night we hung out with J. at the park
after a rainstorm ambushed the city,
when the desert smelled pungent,
and spadefoot toads bleated like goats,
and lightning took its candid
photos in the distance,
and the warm wind crawled up our shorts,
when we took a break from our normal lives,
J. and I kissed.

@themoonforreal
There's nothing you could have said to make her
change her mind.

It Heads On Like a Run On Sentence No One Punctuates

The tribesmen don't come.
I stand out in the desert and watch the moon.
All over the world guys wait
on their last night of boyhood.
The milky sky fades away
above their childhood beds.
Tomorrow, they'll be tested to the edge of their lives,
not all will return.
In a few days' time they'll lie and stare at the moon,
beaten, cut, insulted, praised, pushed,
taught, secluded, included,
changed forever.

If change was only as simple as flipping channels
on a universal remote,
or stepping into a Target dressing room
and coming out with new slacks
and a different attitude.

But my life doesn't change,
no curtain swished close,
no four-gun salute,
no checkered flag

waving,
no dirt thrown on
the coffin,
or starter gun
fired,
no credits
rolling down
from the sky
like overdue rain.

@themoonforreal
The chapters of your life are not labeled and laid
out. That's not how it works.

76. Entrepreneurial kids; lemonade stands, garage sales, baked goods, etc.

77. Painting my face like a skeleton at the All Souls Procession, cracking glow sticks, watching Flam Chen spin fire, reading memorial signs for people who died and feeling thankful to be alive.

78. Remembering good times with my friends who died, they were so young, and now they'll never be here again.

79. Driving through tiny towns at night on the way to my grandparents' house in Wisconsin, passing silos, and fast food chains, street lights streaking in, our tires thudding over interstate pavement, listening to whatever fuzzy radio stations we find, and imagining who the people are in these small towns with their porch lights on.

Third Stone Bridge from the Parking lot

I slip on my baggy shorts, flip flops, and t-shirt,
though I wish there was something else
for me to wear,
another outfit, for another life.
A new skin underneath this old one.
My clothes damp against my wet body,
the air picks up,
my friends still out in the water.
I head down the trail,
to move away from them,
as if they might eavesdrop on my thoughts,
carried through the canyon
in the wind.

I follow the road, alone,
until my hair is almost dry.
How to make my life different, for real?
For this not to be another weekend,
another day, another conversation,
for things to change forever.

@themoonforreal
You make your own change.

Are You with Us?

As we race to the sunset, with the sun in our eyes,
are you lounging with us in the backseat,
dog hair clinging to the upholstery,
your head resting on Matas' and Sci-fi's shoulders?
Are you scaling saguaro trunks
as we watch the sunset
from the square rock in the desert?

Are you loitering with us at Highland Vista Park,
everyone's cars circled around in the glass littered
parking lot,
a wagon train on defense,
speakers booming,
hunting for parties,
making mistakes.
Are you with us in any of these places?

Perhaps
with
distance from the living
you can
tell us
how long
it takes

to bury

those

that

should

not

be dead.

@themoonforreal
There's no rulebook for grieving—
you learn to live with it.

80. One time we drove our RV next to this train in the middle of nowhere. A boy about my age rode in an open railcar and waved at me. I kept imagining what sort of life he lived. Me with my family driving to visit my grandparents, and him alone on a train, not knowing where he's headed. What if we traded places? If my family adopted him and I was the one alone on a speeding train, not sure where I'm going.

Walking Back, 12:43 AM

Wind gusts around mounted trashcans
and through low stone bridges water flows under.
It whistles over cactus thorns,
passes over the thin hairs on our legs,
blows across the muted glimmer of our eyes.
It wrestles bushes, throws tumbleweeds,
and leaves swaying trees to dance dignified.

We hold our arms out as the wind yells past us,
our hair flung over our eyes,
and brushed from our faces.
We walk on, past ranches with horses in the dark,
moonlight reflected on their black eyes,
past the stench of dead animals in bushes,
the far-off whoosh of cars
like solitary waves in search of a shore.
The city lights below us as we stroll back,
stretched between the mountains,
now a valley of light and not sand.
The old pueblo,
without walls around it to keep everyone out.

How to diagnose the urge to speak words I don't
possess?

Don't know how to explain what's inside of me.
I'm a stowaway
in the hard faced breeze.

@themoonforreal
You're not alone in the breeze.

Party Like it's 1999

I smuggle these feelings
wherever I go,
a private breeze carried close to my skin,
through dilapidated house parties,
and backyard piñata fiestas
lined with luminarias and old world punch bowls,
and adobe room wine tastings, and underground
clubs I couldn't sneak into,
and dance clubs where everyone stands against the
walls,
to watch the stilled dance floor.

I ferry this breeze
as I head back to the parties I found,
where guns went off and we huddled under counters
crouched like animals
pissing in frozen woods,
the parties where no one smiles and we nod heads
and exchange few words as though solemn over an
impending death.
I take the breeze with me to late night slick skin
black bottom pool parties,
and to parties where everyone's old and sketchy
and you worry

you'll contract a virus if you lean against the walls,
everyone so messed up, the house feels condemned.
Or at parties where we stand on the roof and make
poor man's fireworks,
where tough guys break fingers hugging each other
and people compare hand drawn tattoos,
fights out back against the chain link fence,
everyone falling into the dust, cursing.
Or parties where we talk to one person
and make jokes
and everyone else spins out of our periphery—
a stationary dust devil around us.

I was there in those parties,
in a hundred back rooms,
in a million conversations,
before umpteen DJs, bobbing my head to albums,
waiting for the party to ignite,
holding my drink over my head, laughing,
busting through wooden fences when the cops came,
hopping walls,
bad music blasting through open windows,
the room crowded, everyone sweaty and drunk.

Everywhere I went, watching,
as if I could find street signs

in people's faces,
gas, food, and lodging
stamped across their foreheads
in green and white.
Or the crucial,
last gas station for 100 miles,
I studied their faces for information,
a clue to indicate where I am
and where I'm headed.
But their faces looked blank,
though they searched my face,
trying to divine if I was friend or foe.
We passed each other, wordless,
through a thousand parties
we've all but forgotten.

@themoonforreal
Friendship will not save you. Where are your
friends now?

81. When the piñata first cracks open and everyone spots the candy inside and I'm next in line. Blindfold tight on my face, stick clenched in my sweaty palms, and all the little kids are desperate to pounce. "Stand back, stand back!" the adults yell, and everyone oohs and ahhs with each swing because it's going to break open any instant. The stick whacks into the piñata and rips through its paper mache skin. Candy gushes out and kids scramble on the ground, frantic out of their minds, starving vultures around fresh prey. And I remove the blindfold a piñata hero.

Move On

Give me a song
I can't stop singing,
give me a forehead
I can sweat,
give me
a tongue
which won't
go dry in
my mouth,
give me
a head
that won't
think
about
itself,
give me a heart
I can't break,
give me
feet
that
won't stop
marching forward.

@themoonforreal
I too wanted a song to sing.

Leaving Sabino Canyon, the Moon Speaks, 1:14 AM

We become human again as we near the parking lot.
The water long dry on us, tired from the walk,
but relaxed.
I start the car, music blares.

"Turn it down," Matas says.

Pulling out of the parking lot, headlight beams slice
through pavement.

Driving down Sunrise,
grocery store lights glare in the dark,
past frozen yogurt shops where summer girls
mop floors in the morning.

The moon skinny-dips in the lukewarm sky.
The air so clear we're made naked in our clothes,
as we race, windows open, under all the night skies
of my short life.
The sky which dumps moon on us,
waits to get noticed by dogs and coyotes,
it shimmers above us, bites its many tongues,
holds off dawn as long as it can,

before it slips into blue before sun up.

The sky which covers us like sleeping children,
because we've acted like children,
though we don't speak the words of children,
or sleep in bodies laden with innocence,
we drive ourselves, and dress ourselves,
and play our dramas like adults
but we've been children all along.

> Wisps of clouds fall away,
> the moon barks down at us,
> "Grow up already,
> I don't want to watch you
> each night
> driving around, bored,
> forever smoking,
> with your big talk
> and small lives."

Dropping Matas & Sci-fi Off

Sci-fi snores
in the backseat.
Probably dreaming
about movie quotes and redheads.

        Matas lights his last cigarette.
        "What are you doing tomorrow?"

"Writing my paper."

We pull up to Sci-fi's house
and nudge him awake—he doesn't have a curfew
so he doesn't worry
about getting grounded for showing up late.

        Sci-fi blinks his eyes open,
        "Where are we?"

"At your house.
And how can this be?"
I say, quoting Dune,
"For he is the Kwisatz Haderach!"

        "Nice."

Sci-fi stumbles
out of the car.

"Next week,
7th & Cherry, for sure."

I head down the street,
Matas lives in the same housing development,
inside the same 10-foot-high cinder block wall.
He takes a long drag on his cigarette.
No one on the street,
every manicured bush and southwestern villa
up to the neighborhood committee's specifications.
The guy in the security cart drives by,
something you'd never find in my neighborhood,
it'd get cart-jacked.

"You alright?" Matas asks.

"Yeah."

The end of his cigarette
crackles as he inhales,
his face illuminated in an
orange glow.

"You wouldn't do what J. did?"

"Never."

Matas holds his hand out the window
to run his fingers through the air.
AC units drone across
the neighborhood.

> We pull up to his house,
> Matas stubs his cigarette out
> in the ashtray.

> "I had to ask,
> you seem like you were
>   somewhere else tonight."

I rest my hands
on the steering wheel,
not sure where to begin.
I could talk non-stop for the rest of my life
and still not reach the bottom of the ache inside me.
"I always liked her."

> "I know."

Matas stands for a moment,
his keys in his hands,
past curfew.
The porch light flips on.

"I gotta go,
see you Monday."

"See you."
I drive off alone.
The empty car full of ghosts
and the words I can't express.

Driving up Kolb, Not Heading Home, 1:43 AM

How many soccer games played on yellow grass,
how many frozen coconut paletas licked,
how many plastic packets of Chiclets chewed,
how many horny toads caught,
to stroke the soft underbelly,
and caress along their chins
so they don't shoot blood from their eyes at me?
How many hours driving empty moon drenched
streets
searching for parties we never found,
how many 64 ounce Big Gulps drank,
how many sci-fi movies rented,
how many crickets kept me awake at night,
how many times the sky changed color overhead,
ravens slumming it into town,
beaks half open tempted to speak?
How many sand rubies collected
in the palm of my hand,
how much AC pumped into the car,
how many goat's head thorns pulled from our dogs'
quivering paws,
how many bikes coasted through the neighborhood,
how many skateboard tricks landed,

how many inches did it rain in this city
since the day I was born?

@themoonforreal
Where are you going?
Why aren't you headed home?

@themoonforreal
Do you want to die out in the
desert like your friend?

@themoonforreal
Are you listening to me?

Detour

I drive to the end of Alvernon,
turn the engine off and stare at the city.
Can't make out anything in particular, even U of A
and downtown
blend together in a mass of lights.

The night bugs whine as I step out of the car
and yank my t-shirt over my head,
because it's still hot.
I need to head out, I'm not ready to drive home yet,
though I'm an hour and three minutes past curfew.

The landscape hushed,
the bushes and critters watch me in bewilderment.
I shouldn't hike in the desert alone because I may
be bitten by a spider
or fall or any number of calamities.
But I go because I need to feel dry wind on my skin,
to feel something wild stir inside me,
the mountains stand firmly in the dark
over our city which grows around us.
Climbing the rocky trail I've hiked so many times
I could draw every pebble.

My flip flops hard slap against my feet
echoes in the canyon, a sound the desert would
never claim as its own.
Hiking the path, hot air close against my skin,
wanting to swallow me in its bottomless belly.
Crickets herald my return
in call and response choruses.
I want to run
though I can't see well in the moonlight.
I want to run, so I run,
although it's stupid,
sprinting along the path,
I find a long stick (an abandoned walking stick, left
by a hiker)
and pick it up
catapulting over rocks,
the stick in my grasp,
wanting to be a tribesman,
with nothing but the landscape,
my stick and a hunt.
Wanting to be primal,
to shed blood and sweat,
to live on instinct,
make no phone calls, send no texts,
responsible only to the sounds of the land,
listen only to the

tingle across my skin
as a rival clansman
approaches.

I stop running
because I'm not
tribal.
I'm not
catching my own food.
If I captured an animal
I wouldn't want to
skin it,
or cook it,
or eat it,
I'd rather go through the drive-through.

@themoonforreal
You are going to find the place
where she died aren't you?

82. Watching bold roadrunners dart about, and horny toads do their short stop and start movements, and snakes on dirt paths never in a rush. And broke guys in my neighborhood bumming cigarettes—all they own is their strut. People drive around at night by the Sabino Jack in the Box, searching for something going on and everyone busy with their stupid phones. Kids so bored they start fights with other schools, anxious for drama. Wanting something to happen that doesn't fade away into another story of a generic weekend past. I want to add a plot to my life and say this is where I'm headed, here is the moral, here's the turning point, the rite of passage where everything changed….. not blurred into something the same as before. I know these people around me. We comment on photos, we text addresses to parties, but they're not my friends in the sense of we understand what's important to each other. I can't explain, there's a part of me this life hasn't reached, a quiet place where I'm not influenced by any of them.

Do the tiny things I enjoy about living
outweigh the persistent numbness?
What are the big things I'm living for?

If I didn't have the moon
who is there for me
when I need them?

End of Alvernon, 2:20 AM

The ground crunches beneath my flip flops.
The eucalyptus tree in the canyon sways.
I hike on uncertain of why I didn't cry at J.'s funeral
but my heart feels as if it's been jumped by a gang
and beaten with sticks.

I wish the ache I felt was not inside me but outside.
A trial I face without whimpering or flinching
like sticking my hands into gloves
filled with fire ants
and I stand there while everyone stares at me.
I put on a brave face, an immovable mask, no one
peeks behind.

But here in the desert alone, it's my heart that stings
and the feeling won't end at dawn with a ritual bath
in an ancient river, or a ceremony, or a feast.
This pain won't end when a shaman, covered in
feathers, says I've suffered enough.

It keeps aching
and I don't know who
I'm putting the brave face on for.
No one watches me

to check if I'll make it through this.
No tribe stands behind me.
There's only my stinging heart
and no medicine to cool the pain
and no clear mark
the ordeal is over.

@themoonforreal
Let go of the history you carry.

On This Rock

J. stood beneath
the whole night sky.

Chalky taste
of pills
on her tongue,
heavy gun
holding her
hand.

Cutting her own
trapdoor
out of the desert.

In the last
minute
of her life,

she looked out
in the windy canyon
and danced.

Google Maps

I climb to the top of the rock, where J. took her life
a week ago,
standing where she last stood,
wanting to begin my life,
not end it.

Flying over the city,
I coast through empty backyards,
with their basketball nets, barbecue pits,
and ocotillo fences,
the drains of their pools full of beetles,
the smell of chlorine wafts into the air around me.

I soar above cut grass
for people in the desert crazy enough to plant grass.
I marvel at deck chairs and dog slobbered tennis
balls lodged under bushes.

Out I fly amongst coyotes and little creeks trickling
down from the mountains,
"Is this where I'm from?"

I shoot into the air, zoom back,
as if I'm a living Google map

that can pull up and watch the city fall into little grids,
and zoom out and the city turns
into splotches of color
and pull back and the border of Arizona leans
against Mexico.

I pull back and America slumbers below me,
all the lights of its cities clump together,
and the seas which splash and kiss its long shores.
I zoom back over North and South America.
Back past the earth's edges with stars out beyond it.
More planets than you can count.
I pull back and the earth becomes another speck
I cannot identify in the dark.
The sun shines, another star in the expanse of sky.
I pull back until there are no features to distinguish
and there, at the final edge, beyond anything you
can describe, I ask,
"Where do I belong in all of this?"
I zoom in, shoot in, race in,
and I'm back on Earth
in a field of high grass,
a breeze blows across me
so calmly I cannot help
but relax.
And though I don't recognize

where I am,
if it's somewhere on the globe
or somewhere inside of myself,
I know, beyond a shadow of a doubt,
I'm home.

Only then
I speak into the wind.

"Goodbye, J."

@themoonforreal
There are those who do more than
stare at me. For them I speak.

83. The red moon while swimming in the bath
    warm ocean in Puerto Peñasco, the super
    moon inching over the horizon and the
    sliver of moon—its claw stuck in the sky.
    Sometimes the moon is my only friend
    and I watch to see what she'll do. Driving
    late at night on silent roads with the moon
    overhead, becoming a foreign creature I
    can't recognize. All those empty towns I
    passed through with the moon for company,
    windows open, air rushing in, the moon
    poking through the clouds, werewolf moons,
    flat moons like the bottom of your coffee
    cup, hunter's moons, half-moons, moons
    so big and bright they'll burst open at first
    nudge—watching the moon from cracked
    car windows, through the dust of dirt roads,
    on railroad tracks, in rain puddles, watching
    the moon, my confidant. The moon I spot in
    the afternoon sky, peeking through the blue,
    a button the sky cannot unfasten.

The Blue Before Dawn Comes and I Drive Home, 3:02 AM

Coasting down Pontatoc,
I dodge red-eyed jackrabbits
bolting across the road.

        If it's a storm of boredom,
        slice it open

The car hums on the solitary road.

        If it's a storm of worry,
        wrestle it to the ground.

Dark sky lifts above me,
porch lights still on,
the city dreams with its ghosts.

        If it's a storm of memories, let it
        pour over me
        and wash away.

Pulling into our driveway
the bees above the front gate buzz.

If it's a storm of longing,
if it's the storm I've waited for,
I'll run through it,
lightning strikes the ground
around me,
wind ripe in my ears,
the desert
fresh with rain.

@themoonforreal

See you tomorrow night.

84. Dancing with J. in the sprinklers, past curfew, sneaking into apartment pools, and kissing her, knowing in another life we'd marry each other, grow old, and move down to Puerto Peñasco to watch the waves all day and make folk art with shells we find strolling the beaches together.

Enzo Jones

2nd Period

World Cultures

Rites of Passage

According to Arnold Van Gennep a rite of passage consists of three parts: 1) separation, 2) transition, 3) reincorporation. In the Xhosa Ceremony, a goat is sacrificed and boys 17-20 are circumcised without any anesthetic. They're sent out naked into the bush with a blanket and must fend for themselves until the wound heals. No medicine is given except the traditional medicine they gather on their own. When they return, if they live through the ordeal, a goat is sacrificed and they throw a party (not like our parties, though).

Mr. Parks, I'm not sure what to tell you about rites of passage. The only initiation I experienced at Rincon is when I walked over the Ranger emblem freshman year and a group of seniors made me push a penny across it with my nose. But it takes more than public embarrassment to make you a man and Van Gennep would snicker and say I wasn't "recognized and incorporated into the group with a new status in the community."

From where I stand there's been a passage of

rites. It all heads on like a run-on sentence no one punctuates or a novel with no chapter breaks.

J. killed herself and she won't be sitting next to me in class on Monday. I've never been close to anyone who died. Yvonne's grandma died but at the funeral I didn't peek in the casket. I walked to Yvonne in the front pew and hugged her and told her, "I'm sorry for your loss." And forgot to look in the casket.

I'm not making any of those remembrance shirts for J. with dates and photographs on the back like when Miguel crashed his motorcycle into a telephone pole. I don't want to make shirts for her, I'd rather acknowledge the people who keep on living. Dying is no way to find happiness. Life, even when it sucks, is still a gift not to waste. That's my remembrance for J., not to give up like she did, but to live until my last breath.

What else can I say? I wrote some poems about it, don't laugh, I know most people think poems are lame, but it didn't make sense to write it any other way. The first one is called Saddling the Toyota Corolla, 6:20 PM.

Acknowledgements

Thank you to my family for their ongoing support and encouragement: Michelle, Odin, Tom, Joey and Jorah.

This book was made possible by a New Works Artist Project Grant from the Arts Foundation for Tucson and Southern Arizona. Thank you for believing in this book and community project. This is a work of fiction inspired by real events growing up in Tucson. Any views or mistakes in representing this period of youth and loss are my own and do not necessarily represent those of the Arts Foundation or anyone else.

To the reader: Just like Envo, if you have "a tiny thing" you enjoy about living and are willing to share it publicly, please email it to me through my website: www.torrananderson.com

Looking forward to hearing from you.

Made in the USA
Lexington, KY
22 November 2019

57525497R00129